MARVEL

SPIDER-MAN

Homecoming

PRELUDE

COLLECTION EDITOR: **JENNIFER GRÜNWALD**
ASSISTANT EDITOR: **CAITLIN O'CONNELL**
ASSOCIATE MANAGING EDITOR: **KATERI WOODY**
EDITOR, SPECIAL PROJECTS: **MARK D. BEAZLEY**
VP PRODUCTION & SPECIAL PROJECTS: **JEFF YOUNGQUIST**
SVP PRINT, SALES & MARKETING: **DAVID GABRIEL**

EDITOR IN CHIEF: **AXEL ALONSO**
CHIEF CREATIVE OFFICER: **JOE QUESADA**
PRESIDENT: **DAN BUCKLEY**
EXECUTIVE PRODUCER: **ALAN FINE**

SPIDER-MAN: HOMECOMING PRELUDE. Contains material originally published in magazine form as SPIDER-MAN: HOMECOMING PRELUDE #1-2, INVINCIBLE IRON MAN (2008) #7, and AMAZING SPIDER-MAN (1963) #2 and #46. First printing 2017. ISBN# 978-1-302-90516-3. Published by MARVEL WORLDWIDE, INC., a subsidiary of MARVEL ENTERTAINMENT, LLC. OFFICE OF PUBLICATION: 135 West 50th Street, New York, NY 10020. Copyright © 2017 MARVEL No similarity between any of the names, characters, persons, and/or institutions in this magazine with those of any living or dead person or institution is intended, and any such similarity which may exist is purely coincidental. **Printed in the U.S.A.** DAN BUCKLEY, President, Marvel Entertainment; JOE QUESADA, Chief Creative Officer; TOM BREVOORT, SVP of Publishing; DAVID BOGART, SVP of Business Affairs & Operations, Publishing & Partnership; C.B. CEBULSKI, VP of Brand Management & Development, Asia; DAVID GABRIEL, SVP of Sales & Marketing, Publishing; JEFF YOUNGQUIST, VP of Production & Special Projects; DAN CARR, Executive Director of Publishing Technology; ALEX MORALES, Director of Publishing Operations; SUSAN CRESPI, Production Manager; STAN LEE, Chairman Emeritus. For information regarding advertising in Marvel Comics or on Marvel.com, please contact Vit DeBellis, Integrated Sales Manager, at vdebellis@marvel.com. For Marvel subscription inquiries, please call 888-511-5480. **Manufactured between 3/31/2017 and 5/2/2017 by QUAD/GRAPHICS WASECA, WASECA, MN, USA.**

10 9 8 7 6 5 4 3 2 1

MARVEL

SPIDER-MAN

Homecoming

PRELUDE

BASED ON THE **CAPTAIN AMERICA: CIVIL WAR**
SCREENPLAY BY **CHRISTOPHER MARKUS & STEPHEN MCFEELY**

WRITER: **WILL CORONA PILGRIM**
ARTIST: **TODD NAUCK**
COLOR ARTISTS: **VERONICA GANDINI** WITH **JAY DAVID RAMOS** (#2)
LETTERER: **VC's TRAVIS LANHAM**
EDITOR: **MARK BASSO**

MARVEL STUDIOS
DIRECTOR OF PRODUCTION & DEVELOPMENT: **TRINH TRAN**
DIRECTOR OF PRODUCTION & DEVELOPMENT: **ERIC H. CARROLL**
VP PRODUCTION & DEVELOPMENT: **NATE MOORE**
SVP PRODUCTION & DEVELOPMENT: **JEREMY LATCHAM**
PRESIDENT: **KEVIN FEIGE**

SPIDER-MAN CREATED BY **STAN LEE & STEVE DITKO**

SPIDER-MAN: HOMECOMING
PRELUDE #1

BUCHAREST.

"...I'M SURE CAP'S GOT A HANDLE ON IT."

BUCKY, STOP. LET ME TAKE CARE OF THIS.

ALL OF YOU STAND DOWN. NOW.

WAR MACHINE
Jim Rhodes

HEY, EASY, FELLAS. *EASY!* WE'RE THE GOOD GUYS HERE.

NO, SAM. SINCE YOU AND STEVE DIDN'T SIGN THE SOKOVIA ACCORDS, THE TWO OF YOU ARE OUTSIDE THE LAW ON THIS ONE.

CONGRATULATIONS, CAP. YOU'RE A *CRIMINAL.*

YOU'RE COMING WITH ME.

YOU TOO, YOUR *HIGHNESS.*

BLACK PANTHER
King T'Challa

THE FALCON
Sam Wilson

THUMPA-
THUMPA-
THUMPA

NNNNNNNN...!

CREAK-
CRACK-
CRACK

HK! BUCKY. NO...

SPLASH

LET'S HOPE YOU'LL COME TO YOUR SENSES WHEN YOU WAKE UP.

QUEENS.

UM, HEH, WHAT...WHAT ARE YOU DOING...HEY! UH, UM, I'M--I'M PETER.

TONY.

WHAT ARE YOU...WHAT ARE YOU...WHAT ARE YOU DOING HERE?

IT'S ABOUT TIME WE MET. YOU'VE BEEN GETTING MY EMAILS, RIGHT?

THE SEPTEMBER FOUNDATION.

RIGHT.

YEAH. REMEMBER WHEN YOU APPLIED?

YEAH.

I APPROVED, SO NOW WE'RE IN BUSINESS.

YOU KEEPING SECRETS FROM ME NOW?

WELL, I JUST--I JUST KNOW HOW MUCH YOU LOVE SURPRISES, SO I THOUGHT I WOULD LET YOU KNOW... ANYWAY, WHAT DID I APPLY FOR?

ARE THOSE WINGS CARBON FIBER?

IS THIS STUFF COMING *OUT* OF YOU?

THAT WOULD EXPLAIN THE RIGIDITY-FLEXIBILITY RATIO, WHICH, GOTTA SAY, THAT'S *AWESOME*, MAN.

I DON'T KNOW IF YOU'VE BEEN IN A FIGHT BEFORE, BUT THERE'S USUALLY NOT THIS MUCH *TALKING*.

ALL RIGHT, SORRY. MY BAD.

GUYS, LOOK, I'D LOVE TO KEEP THIS UP, BUT I'VE ONLY GOT ONE JOB HERE TODAY AND I GOTTA IMPRESS MR. STARK, SO I'M REALLY SORRY.

WHAT?

GYAAAAH!

YOU COULDN'T HAVE CALLED YOUR LITTLE DRONE IN *EARLIER*?

I HATE YOU.

WHAM

YES! THAT WAS AWESOME!

THAT WAS--

SM ACK

THE INVINCIBLE
IRON MAN

FRACTION
LARROCA
D'ARMATA

MARVEL
7
.com

TEANECK, N.J.

IT'S ONE THING TO MAKE A LITTLE NOISE IN JERSEY CITY...

NOT SURE HOW WE CAN KEEP THIS QUIET IF WHEELE RUNS.

WHEELE'S A GOOD GUY. HE'S STARTED SUPPORT GROUPS FOR GUYS TRYING TO GET OUT OF THE LIFE--

HE'S GOT BLACK MARKET CONNECTIONS TO SUPER-W.M.D. NETWORKS.

--BUT I'M SAYING, HE'S A GOOD GUY. JUST A LITTLE OFF THE WAGON, Y'KNOW?

NO SUCH THING.

SO WHAT'S YOUR PLAN?

FIVE MINUTES.

WATCH AND WAIT AND WONDER.

DING--

KRRRSH

I CAN'T GO BACK TO JAIL--!

TONY STARK!

TONY STARK!

OHMIGOD--

LOOK AT THAT TUX--

TONY! DADDY SAID THERE WAS *NO WAY* YOU'D COME TO MY BIRTHDAY PARTY BUT I TOLD HIM HE WAS WRONG AND THAT I KNEW YOU WOULD COME AND--

--MISS THE SUPER-SWEETEST BIRTHDAY OF THE MOST AMAZING GIRL ON ALL OF LONG ISLAND? PLEASE.

MANY HAPPY RETURNS, DOLL.

THANK YOU, TONY. WHAT'D YOU GET ME? I HOPE IT'S *BIG.* OR AT LEAST EXPENSIVE.

OH, IT'S *BOTH*--

--BUT WHAT ABOUT YOUR *OLD MAN?*

IN THE *BASEMENT* WITH HIS *TOYS.*

WHERE HE *ALWAYS* IS, *DUH.*

THANKS, LOVE.

HEY, *WAIT*--!

YOU KNOW WHAT I MEAN? LIKE OLD TIMES. ONLY THING MISSING WAS, LIKE, A BAG OF JEWELRY. MAYBE A BIG GUY DRESSED AS AN ANIMAL.

NOBODY *DIED*. THAT'S WHAT I LIKED MOST OF ALL. WE SHOULD DO IT MORE OFTEN.

YOU'RE BREAKING. THE LAW. PERIOD. UNLESS YOU WANT TO REGISTER, THE KIND OF TROUBLE THIS KIND OF STUFF WOULD CAUSE ME...

IT'S ONE MORE THING. AND I JUST CAN'T *TAKE* ONE MORE THING RIGHT NOW.

THIS--ALL OF THIS--STARK, S.H.I.E.L.D... IT'S ALL JUST POISED ON THE RAZOR'S EDGE. STANE'S ATTACKS, THE RIFTS BETWEEN THE GOOD GUYS, THE BAD GUYS CONSOLIDATING--

I DON'T KNOW IF I'M STRONG ENOUGH AND SMART ENOUGH TO KEEP IT TOGETHER.

YYYYEAH. WELL.

YOU'RE A SMART GUY. YOU'LL FIGURE IT OUT, HUH?

TAKE CARE, MR. STARK. GOOD LUCK WITH--

WELL, WITH RUNNING THE WORLD, I GUESS.

YEAH.

YEAH, OKAY.

...JANITORS AND ENGINEERS AND CONSTRUCTION GUYS AND GLASS REPAIR GUYS AND DATA RECOVERY GUYS AND GUYS THAT WORK WITH SCIENCES SO WEIRD IT SOUNDS LIKE SCIENCE FICTION...

AND YOU KNOW WHAT I FOUND?

WHAT?

THEY ALL HAD THE SAME THING TO SAY.

THEY'RE ALL TERRIFIED AND WORRIED. SOME FOLKS'RE STILL IN SHOCK.

MM.

SO NO CLIFFORD POLLACK?

CLIFTON POLLARD.

HIM TOO.

NOT SO MUCH.

WHAT ABOUT YOU? GET YOUR SHOT?

I THINK SO. I GOT-- I GOT A SHOT.

WELL? LET'S SEE IT.

PETER, I--

WATCH THE ROAD.

ARE YOU KIDDING ME?

THE ROAD, SIR.

HOW DID YOU GET THAT SHOT? HOW DID--ARE YOU KIDDING ME!?!

WE GOTTA GET BACK TO THE CITY.

WE GOTTA GET THIS OUT--TODAY, PARKER--

REALLY? YOU THINK IT'S OKAY?

FRONT LINE

MORNING EDITION - 50 CENTS   **WEDNESDAY, NOVEMBER 5, 2008**

THE HEAD THAT WEARS THE CROWN

FEATURE ARTICLE
BY BEN URICH

PHOTOGRAPH BY PETER PARKER

LONG ISLAND–The fires at Stark Industries have been burning for a week now. It smells like burnt fish and hot dust. They tell you it's all the wiring that melted when a high-tech lunatic named Ezekiel Stane tried to wipe Tony Stark, and Stark Industries, off the face of the earth.

And Stark, as anyone with a television can tell you, hasn't slept since the fires started.

The mood at Stark Industries, or what's left of it, is that of a bereaved family, only instead of mourning the passing of a beloved patriarch or doddering old aunt, this is a family dozens of lives smaller, stolen in an instant by an inhuman monster, in an inhumanly monstrous moment of cruelty. There are not words to adequately explain the loss.

Stark employees, as they'll tell you if you give them half a second, tend to work for Stark as long as possible. Every employee I spoke with--from the janitors to the particle physicists--would introduce themselves to me, then rattle off their tenure at Stark like it was their last name.

"I can't imagine a world without Stark Industries."

Continued on pg. 19

TONY STARK AT THE LONG ISLAND FACILITY

MORE HEADLINES

"CLIFTON POLLARD"
THE FIVE NIGHTMARES: EPILOGUE

BY MATT FRACTION & SALVADOR LARROCA

FRANK D'ARMATA – colorist; VC'S JOE CARAMAGNA – letterer;
ALEJANDRO ARBONA – assistant editor; WARREN SIMONS – editor;
JOE QUESADA – editor in chief; DAN BUCKLEY – publisher

SPIDER-MAN

"DUEL TO THE DEATH WITH The VULTURE!"

THE MOST COLORFUL SUPER-HERO OF ALL... *SPIDER-MAN!* HIS NAME MAKES THE UNDERWORLD TREMBLE! BUT THERE IS *ONE* WHO DOES NOT TREMBLE! WHAT FANTASTIC POWER CAN *THE VULTURE* HAVE WHICH MAKES HIM SO SURE HE CAN DEFEAT... *SPIDER-MAN?*

SCRIPT:
STAN LEE
ART:
STEVE DITKO
LETTERING:
JOHN DUFFY

FOR DAYS, A NEW AND OMINOUS DANGER HAS MENACED THE VAST CITY OF NEW YORK! NO MAN KNOWS WHERE HE'LL STRIKE NEXT! NO ONE CAN COPE WITH THIS NEW, AWESOME THREAT! WITHOUT WARNING, WITHOUT THE SLIGHTEST SOUND, HE STRIKES!

FOR THIS IS -- *THE VULTURE!*

IT'S *THE VULTURE!* HE STOLE MY BRIEFCASE -- WITH A FORTUNE IN BONDS! *HELP!!*

I'VE *READ* ABOUT HIM--BUT NEVER EXPECTED TO *SEE* HIM!

I *DIDN'T BELIEVE* IT! I THOUGHT HE DIDN'T EXIST!

IT'S IMPOSSIBLE! IT CAN'T BE! HOW CAN HE *FLY* -- WITHOUT A SOUND--WITHOUT ANY EFFORT! HE'S MORE LIKE A GIGANTIC BIRD OF PREY THAN A HUMAN!

AND, IN THE EXECUTIVE SUITE OF THE POWERFUL *JAMESON PUBLICATIONS*, MR. J. JONAH JAMESON IS ON HIS USUAL RAMPAGE...

I WANT TO DEVOTE THE NEXT ENTIRE ISSUE OF *NOW MAGAZINE* TO *THE VULTURE!* HE'S BIG NEWS! EVERYONE WANTS TO READ ABOUT HIM!

BUT KEEP PRINTING STORIES ABOUT *SPIDER-MAN* ALSO! I'LL NEVER REST TILL THAT DANGEROUS MENACE IS DESTROYED!

J. JONAH JAMESON PUBLISH

NOW MAGAZINE

IS *THIS* THE ONLY PHOTO WE HAVE OF *THE VULTURE?* WHAT'S THE MATTER WITH YOU MEN? WHAT AM I *PAYING* YOU FOR? THE PUBLIC WANTS TO *SEE* HIM!

BUT, MR. JAMESON, *NOBODY* CAN GET PICTURES OF HIM! HE'S GONE BEFORE ANY PHOTOGRAPHER CAN GET TO HIM! WE HAVE ONLY AN ARTIST'S DRAWING!

NO MORE EXCUSES! GET ME PICTURES OF *THE VULTURE--* OR I'LL GET SOME NEW EDITORS!

NOW

MENACE

MEANWHILE, IN A NEARBY HIGH SCHOOL, PETER PARKER OVERHEARS AN INTERESTING DISCUSSION AS THE YOUNG SCIENCE MAJOR PERFORMS AN EXPERIMENT IN THE LAB...

BOY! I'D LIKE TO SEE A CLOSE-UP PHOTO OF *THE VULTURE!!*

A PHOTO OF *THE VULTURE* WOULD BE WORTH A *FORTUNE!* NOBODY CAN GET CLOSE ENOUGH TO HIM TO SNAP ONE!

SAY! THAT'S AN IDEA! I NEVER *THOUGHT* OF IT BEFORE! MAGAZINES PAY BIG MONEY FOR HARD-TO-GET PHOTOS! AND *I* KNOW HOW TO GET THEM

NOW

As soon as school ends, the excited teen-ager rushes home to his Aunt May and is delighted to learn...

And then, in the privacy of his room, Peter Parker changes into the most dramatic costumed figure of all -- that of SPIDER-MAN!...

Meanwhile, in a carefully-prepared hideout on the outskirts of the city...

AFTER MAKING CERTAIN HE IS NOT OBSERVED, *THE VULTURE* DARTS FROM HIS HIDING PLACE ATOP AN ABANDONED SILO IN STATEN ISLAND, JUST A FEW SECONDS FROM THE HEART OF MANHATTEN...

NOW FOR THE FIRST PART OF MY INGENIOUS PLAN!

SECONDS LATER, ATOP AN APARTMENT HOUSE WHERE HE HAD BEEN CHECKING HIS CAMERA, *SPIDER-MAN'S* AMAZING SPIDER SENSES PICK UP A STRANGE SENSATION...

SOMETHING COMING THROUGH THE AIR--BUT MAKING NO SOUND!... CAN'T BE A PLANE...

NOT NOTICING THE POWERFUL FIGURE ON THE ROOF TOP, *THE VULTURE* SWEEPS PAST...

THEY'LL *NEVER* FIGURE OUT HOW I'M GOING TO STEAL THOSE DIAMONDS!

I'VE GOT EVERYONE COMPLETELY BAFFLED! NO ONE HAS YET DISCOVERED HOW I MANAGE TO *FLY* WITH THESE ARTIFICIAL WINGS!

WHAT LUCK!... IT'S *THE VULTURE!*

I'LL TOSS SOME MESSAGES WHERE THEY'LL DO THE MOST GOOD!

THE FIRST ONE IS FOR THE *JAMESON PUBLISH-ING COMPANY* BUILDING!

MY NEXT MESSAGE IS FOR THE RADIO NETWORK! NOTHING I LIKE BETTER THAN TAUNTING MY ENEMIES!

C RADIO

AND, FINALLY, ONE FOR THE POLICE CHIEF HIM-SELF! I'LL BE GONE BEFORE THEY HAVE A CHANCE TO READ THEM!

THE VULTURE HAS NEVER FAILED TO CARRY OUT A THREAT YET!

BUT WE *MUST* GO AHEAD WITH THE TRANSFER OF THE DIAMONDS! WE CAN'T LET THE CITY THINK THAT ONE CRIMINAL CAN MAKE US CHANGE OUR PLANS!

I SHALL STEAL THE DIAMOND SHIPMENT FROM UNDER YOUR NOSES!
The Vulture

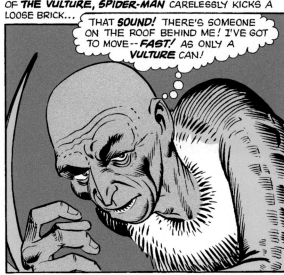

NOW THAT I HAVE DISPOSED OF THAT TEMPORARY INTERRUPTION, I'LL CARRY OUT STEP *TWO* OF MY MASTER PLAN!

MEANWHILE, INSIDE THE TANK, THE SHOCK OF HITTING THE COLD WATER INSTANTLY REVIVES THE POWERFUL *SPIDER-MAN...*

THE VULTURE SOMEHOW TRAPPED ME INSIDE THIS WATER TANK!

WELL, I'VE ONLY MYSELF TO BLAME FOR BEING SO CARELESS!

I'LL JUST SHOOT MY WEB TOWARDS THE TOP AND... *OH, NO!* THE EJECTOR IS EMPTY!

I FORGOT TO REFILL IT SINCE I USED IT LAST! I'VE BEEN SO BUSY WITH THAT CAMERA--! I'VE GOT TO TRY SOMETHING ELSE!

CAN'T CLIMB TO THE TOP--IT'S TOO WET AND SLIMY EVEN FOR *ME* TO GET A TOEHOLD ON!

BUT I SURE AS SHOOTING CAN'T STAY AFLOAT HERE MUCH LONGER!

NOT A PLEASANT CHOICE--I'LL EITHER DROWN OR SUFFOCATE IN HERE!

WAIT A MINUTE! WHAT'S *WRONG* WITH ME? WHY DON'T I USE MY HEAD? I CAN GET OUT OF HERE!

MY MUSCLES ARE FAR STRONGER THAN AN ORDINARY HUMAN'S! THERE'S ONE LITTLE TRICK THAT ONLY THE *SPIDER-MAN* CAN PERFORM!

ALL I'VE GOT TO DO IS REACH THE BOTTOM, SQUAT DOWN, AND PREPARE TO HURL MYSELF UPWARD...

...LIKE *THIS!!*

DID IT!!

I MAY NOT BE ABLE TO FLY LIKE *THE VULTURE* -- BUT MY SPIDER STRENGTH HASN'T LET ME DOWN *YET!*

MY LUCK'S STILL HOLDING OUT-- HERE'S MY CAMERA!

SURE IS UNBELIEVABLE HOW *THE VULTURE* MANAGES TO FLY SO SWIFTLY! I'D SURE LIKE TO FIGURE OUT HOW HE *DOES* IT!

LATER, IN HIS ROOM AGAIN...

THE PICTURES CAME OUT FINE! NOW, WHOM DO I SELL THEM TO? JONAH JAMESON, THE PUBLISHER OF *NOW* MAGAZINE HATES *SPIDER-MAN!* I'D GET A KICK OUT OF MAKING *HIM* PAY GOOD DOUGH FOR MY PICTURES WITHOUT KNOWING *I'M* THE PHOTOGRAPHER!

NOW 25¢
SPIDER-MAN MUST BE CAUGHT!

ORIGINALLY, I DESIGNED MY *SPIDER-MAN* COSTUME JUST TO GIVE ME SOME COLOR, SO THAT I COULD MAKE MONEY AS AN ENTERTAINER! BUT, IF...

...I'M REALLY GOING TO BE A SECRET ADVENTURER, I'VE GOT TO MAKE SOME CHANGES! FIRST, I'LL ADD AN EXTRA WEB-FLUID CAPSULE, SO I ALWAYS HAVE ENOUGH SPIDER-WEBBING ON HAND!

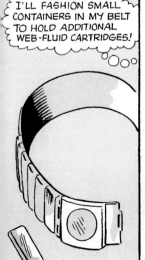

I'LL FASHION SMALL CONTAINERS IN MY BELT TO HOLD ADDITIONAL WEB-FLUID CARTRIDGES!

THEN, WHEN I GET PAID FOR MY PICTURES, I'LL BUY A SPECIAL MINIATURE CAMERA TO SECRETLY ATTACH TO THE BELT BUCKLE!

THERE! THE WHOLE CONTRAPTION FITS UNDER MY SHIRT, WHERE IT'S OUT OF SIGHT, AND DOESN'T INTERFERE WITH MY MOVEMENTS!

AND NOW, I'VE GOT A HUNCH I KNOW THE SECRET OF *THE VULTURE'S* POWER OF FLIGHT! I'LL JUST WORK ON A LITTLE DEVICE WHICH MAY COME IN HANDY NEXT TIME WE MEET!

7

LONG HOURS LATER...

:WHEW: THAT WAS TOUGHER THAN I EXPECTED, BUT IT'S FINISHED NOW!

I WON'T KNOW IF IT'LL WORK TILL I TRY IT-- BUT RIGHT NOW, I'M GONNA GET SOME SHUT-EYE!

THE NEXT DAY, J. JONAH JAMESON RECEIVES AN EXCITING PHONE CALL...

WHAT'S THAT?? YOU'VE GOT SOME EXCLUSIVE PHOTOS OF THE VULTURE THAT YOU WANT TO SELL?? WELL, DON'T WASTE TIME TALKING! GET OVER HERE RIGHT AWAY!

JOE, HAVE THEM STOP THE PRESSES!

AND SOON...

SORRY, MR. JAMESON CANNOT SEE ANYBODY RIGHT NOW! HE'S HAVING AN IMPORTANT CONFERENCE!

THESE PICTURES ARE SENSATIONAL-- GREAT! BUT HOW'D A KID LIKE YOU GET THEM?

SORRY, SIR! I'LL SELL THEM TO YOU ON CONDITION THAT YOU NEVER ASK ME THAT QUESTION!

OKAY, OKAY! YOU CAN HAVE YOUR LITTLE SECRET! IT DOESN'T MATTER HOW YOU GOT THEM! THE POINT IS, THESE PICTURES WILL MAKE THE NEXT ISSUE OF NOW A SELL-OUT! I'LL ISSUE A CHECK TO YOU IMMEDIATELY!

AND REMEMBER, MR. JAMESON, I DON'T WANT MY NAME USED! YOU CAN MERELY GIVE CREDIT TO A NOW MAGAZINE STAFF PHOTOGRAPHER!

SURE, MY BOY, SURE! AND IF YOU GET ANY MORE GREAT PICTURES, REMEMBER TO GIVE ME FIRST CRACK AT THEM! WE'RE ALWAYS IN THE MARKET FOR SENSATIONAL PHOTOS! IN FACT...

... IF YOU CAN EVER GET A PICTURE OF THAT PUBLIC MENACE, SPIDER-MAN--

BROTHER, WOULDN'T YOU BE SURPRISED IF YOU KNEW!

THE NEXT DAY, AS SCHOOL LETS OUT...

C'MON, PETER! WE'RE ALL GOING TO WATCH THEM MOVE THE DIAMONDS FROM THE PARK AVENUE JEWELRY EXCHANGE! WE'RE HOPING TO GET A GLIMPSE OF THE VULTURE!

DON'T BE SCARED, BOOKWORM--WE'LL PROTECT YOU!

YOU DON'T REALLY THINK THE VULTURE WOULD DARE TRY ANYTHING WITH ALL THE POLICE THERE, DO YOU?

GOSH! THE WHOLE AREA IS CORDONED OFF! AND LOOK-- T.V. CAMERAS, NEWSPAPERMEN, POLICE! IT'S LIKE A *CARNIVAL!*

THE VULTURE WOULD BE *NUTS* TO TRY ANYTHING WITH A CROWD LIKE *THIS* AROUND! THIS IS *ONE* TIME HE WON'T MAKE GOOD HIS BOAST!

IT *IS* HARD TO SEE HOW *THE VULTURE* COULD HAVE A *CHANCE* AT THE JEWELS UNDER THESE CONDITIONS! THERE ARE POLICE ON EVERY ROOF, AND AN ARMED HELICOPTER FLYING OVERHEAD!

I'D BETTER MAKE MYSELF SCARCE! IF I HAVE TO CHANGE TO *SPIDER-MAN,* I WON'T BE ABLE TO DO IT IN THE MIDDLE OF THIS MOB!

LOOK, GANG! LITTLE PETEY IS CHICKENING OUT! GUESS THE EXCITEMENT IS TOO MUCH FOR HIS DELICATE LITTLE SELF!

MINUTES LATER, THE VALUABLE JEWELRY SHIPMENT STARTS ITS CROSSTOWN CONVOY, ACCOMPANIED BY PATROL CARS AND THE POLICE WHIRLYBIRD FOLLOWING ABOVE...

I WISH *THE VULTURE WOULD* MAKE A TRY FOR THOSE DIAMONDS, CHUCK! WE'D NAB 'IM FOR *SURE!*

YEAH, BUT HE WON'T SHOW! HE'S TOO SMART FOR THAT!

IT'S ALL CLEAR! START BRINGING THE JEWELS OUT!

NOT A SIGN OF *THE VULTURE!* HE *KNOWS* HE WOULDN'T HAVE A CHANCE!

9

THE SKY'S CLEAR EXCEPT FOR OUR OWN CHOPPER UP THERE! LOOKS LIKE THE WHOLE THING WAS A FALSE ALARM!

BUT STAY ALERT ANYHOW! WITH A CHARACTER LIKE *THE VULTURE*, YOU NEVER KNOW *WHAT'S* GONNA HAPPEN NEXT!

GENTLEMEN, YOU ARE SO *RIGHT!* AND NOW *I'LL* TAKE THOSE DIAMONDS!

THE VULTURE!! BUT HOW--?

WE EXPECTED AN ATTACK FROM *ABOVE!*

BEFORE THE STARTLED OFFICERS CAN FIRE, THE WILY *VULTURE* PLUMMETS BACK UNDERGROUND, DROPPING THE MANHOLE COVER INTO PLACE ABOVE HIM! THEN...

I'LL BE MILES AWAY BEFORE THEY CAN EVEN LIFT THAT MANHOLE COVER!

AND THEY'LL NEVER KNOW *WHICH* OF THESE TWISTING TUNNELS I'M FLYING THROUGH!

A SHORT TIME LATER, AT THE OTHER END OF TOWN A TRIUMPHANT *VULTURE* DECIDES TO LEAVE HIS UNDERGROUND LAIR AS DRAMATICALLY AS POSSIBLE...

LOOK--THE *VULTURE!!* HE JUST FLEW OUT OF THE SUBWAY TUNNEL!

THIS WILL GIVE THE FOOLS SOMETHING TO TALK ABOUT FOR YEARS TO COME!

HOW *SIMPLE* IT WAS! IT WORKED LIKE A CHARM!

NOW I'LL HAVE VANISHED OVER THE ROOF-TOPS BEFORE THE POLICE CAN EVEN BEGIN TO CONVERGE AT THIS POINT!

UPTOWN SUBWAY

MEANWHILE, LEARNING WHAT HAS OCCURRED PETER PARKER MANAGES TO FIND A DESERTED ALLEY, AND THE MOVING WITH BLINDING SPEED...

HE *DID* IT!

HE FOOLED EVERYONE -- EVEN *ME!* BUT I'LL FIND HIM! IF I CAN GET SOME *NEW* PICTURES OF HIM *NOW*, I'LL BE ABLE TO NAME MY OWN PRICE FOR THEM!

SPEAK FOR *YOURSELF,* MISTER! THE SKY IS *MY* ELEMENT AS MUCH AS YOURS! JUST *WATCH!!*

I CAN ALWAYS SAVE MYSELF BY SHOOTING MY WEB AT A NEARBY BUILDING-- LIKE *THIS!*

AS FOR *THE VULTURE,* HE'LL MANAGE TO BREAK HIS FALL BY SPIRALING DOWN, BUT HE'S GONNA HAVE A TOUGH TIME EVER USING THOSE WINGS AGAIN!

HERE COMES THE POLICE HELICOPTER! THEY MUST HAVE SIGHTED US WHEN WE WERE BATTLING! THIS IS MY CHANCE TO GET SOME EXCLUSIVE PIX OF THE CAPTURE OF *THE VULTURE!*

TAKE 'ER DOWN, CHARLIE! WE WERE *RIGHT!* IT *IS* THE VULTURE!

CAN'T GET UP! WIND KNOCKED OUT OF ME! WHAT'LL I *DO--??*

POLICE

IF *THIS* DOESN'T TAKE THE CAKE! WHO EVER THOUGHT WE'D BE ABLE TO CAPTURE *THE VULTURE* SO NICE AND EASY?!! WHAT HAPPENED, FELLA? DID YOU HAVE A TAILSPIN?

PLEASE-- NO JOKES!

THESE PICTURES SHOULD BE PRIZE-WINNERS!

⑬

A STORY HAS TO START SOMEWHERE, SO LET'S BEGIN OURS IN THE SCIENCE LAB OF MIDTOWN HIGH, WHERE WE FIND PETER PARKER HARD AT WORK WHILE...

GOSH, I THOUGHT CLASS WOULD **NEVER** END TODAY! I COULDN'T BEAR LOOKING AT ONE MORE TEST TUBE OR BUNSEN BURNER!

QUIET! YOU'LL BREAK PETER'S HEART! **HE** CAN'T BEAR TO BE **PARTED** FROM THEM!

THERE'S THE BOY I WAS TELLING YOU ABOUT, DOCTOR! HE'S PETER PARKER, OUR TOP SCIENCE STUDENT!

PETER, PROFESSOR COBBWELL HAS ASKED ME TO RECOMMEND A STUDENT WHO COULD HELP HIM WITH SOME RESEARCH OVER THE WEEK-END, AND I WAS WONDERING--?

GOSH! A CHANCE TO WORK WITH THE MOST FAMOUS ELECTRONICS EXPERT IN TOWN? I'D BE **DELIGHTED**, SIR!

THANK YOU, MY BOY! I HAVE SOME URGENT EXPERIMENTS TO PERFORM, AND WILL APPRECIATE YOUR ASSISTANCE!

HERE IS MY ADDRESS, SON! ON YOUR WAY OVER TOMORROW, PLEASE STOP AT THE RADIO REPAIR SHOP AND PICK UP A SMALL RADIO FOR ME! I HAD SOME NEW TUBES PUT IN IT!

SURE, I'LL BE GLAD TO DOCTOR COBBWELL!

MINUTES LATER, WHEN THE STUDENTS ARE ALONE AGAIN...

WELL WELL! SO TEACHER'S PET IS GONNA HELP THE NICE LITTLE DOCTOR WITH SOME EXPERIMENTS THIS WEEK-END, EH? WHILE US OTHER DUMBHEADS WASTE TIME HAVING DATES AND LIVIN' IT UP!

KNOCK IT OFF, FLASH! YOU'RE DARN **RIGHT** I'D JUMP AT THE CHANCE TO WORK WITH A BRILLIANT MAN LIKE DOCTOR COBBWELL! AS FOR YOU BEING A DUMBHEAD, IT'S NOTHING TO BE ASHAMED OF! YOU WERE JUST **BORN** THAT WAY!

THEN, BEFORE THE ANGRY FLASH THOMPSON CAN THINK OF A SUITABLE RETORT, PETER PARKER IS GONE! AND, THE NEXT DAY, AT HOME...

I'D BETTER TAKE MY **SPIDER-MAN** OUTFIT! NEVER KNOW **WHEN** I'LL NEED IT! BESIDES, I FEEL ALMOST UNDRESSED WITHOUT IT!

HMMM, HERE'S THE PLACE THE DOC WANTED ME TO PICK UP HIS RADIO!

THE TINKERER REPAIR SHOP-- SURE IS AN OFF-BEAT NAME! WONDER WHAT KIND OF KOOKIE CHARACTER RUNS IT?

TINKERER

INSIDE THE SHOP...

I'M THE **TINKERER!** WHAT CAN I DO FOR YOU, MY BOY?

I'M HERE TO PICK UP A RADIO FOR DR. COBBWELL!

OH YES! DOCTOR COBBWELL! JUST A MINUTE -- I'LL GET IT!

BOY, I SURE CALLED IT RIGHT! HE LOOKS LIKE A CHARACTER STRAIGHT OUT OF GRIMM'S FAIRY TALES!

THEN, SUDDENLY...

STRANGE... MY SPIDER SENSE PICKS UP ODD ELECTRIC IMPULSES! MUST BE COMING FROM HIS TESTING EQUIPMENT!

I'VE GOT TO STOP GETTING SO SUSPICIOUS ALL THE TIME! THE TINKERER LOOKS ABOUT AS DANGEROUS AS A SECOND-HAND CREAMPUFF!

MEANWHILE, IN A SOUND-PROOFED BASEMENT WORKROOM, DIRECTLY UNDER THE SHOP...

DR. COBBWELL IS READY FOR HIS RADIO! IT IS ONE OF **SPECIAL** JOBS!

GOOD! I HAVE JUST FINISHED IT! HE MAY HAVE IT NOW!

I HAVE INSERTED OUR SPECIAL DEVICE! HE WILL NEVER SUSPECT THAT THIS IS NOW MUCH **MORE** THAN A SIMPLE RADIO!

SO FAR NONE OF OUR "SPECIAL" CUSTOMERS SUSPECTS WHAT WE HAVE DONE TO THEIR RADIOS WHILE WE WERE SUPPOSED TO BE REPAIRING THEM!

NATURALLY! OUR PLAN MUST BE COMPLETELY SECRET, UNTIL WE ARE READY TO STRIKE!

3

AND THEN, AFTER THE LONG CLIMB UPSTAIRS AGAIN...

YOU MEAN YOU ONLY CHARGE A **DIME** TO FIX RADIOS?? BUT--

TUT TUT, MY BOY! I **LIKE** TO GIVE BARGAINS! THEY BRING ME IN LOTS OF CUSTOMERS!

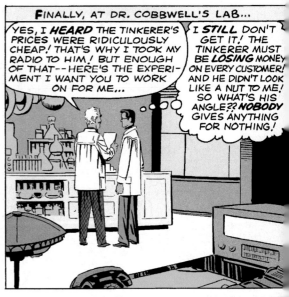

FINALLY, AT DR. COBBWELL'S LAB...

YES, I **HEARD** THE TINKERER'S PRICES WERE RIDICULOUSLY CHEAP! THAT'S WHY I TOOK MY RADIO TO HIM! BUT ENOUGH OF THAT--HERE'S THE EXPERIMENT I WANT YOU TO WORK ON FOR ME...

I **STILL** DON'T GET IT! THE TINKERER MUST BE **LOSING** MONEY ON EVERY CUSTOMER! AND HE DIDN'T LOOK LIKE A NUT TO ME! SO WHAT'S HIS ANGLE?? **NOBODY** GIVES ANYTHING FOR NOTHING!

THIS IS BATTY! I'VE **GOT** TO FORGET THE TINKERER AND CONCENTRATE ON WHAT I'M DOING!

BUT SOMETHING ABOUT HIM KEEPS STICKIN' IN MY CRAW!

WAIT! I KNOW! THOSE ELECTRICAL IMPULSES WHICH I SENSED IN HIS SHOP! **NOW** I SENSE THEM **HERE!**

THE PART OF ME WHICH IS **SPIDER-MAN** IS REACTING SUSPICIOUSLY TO THEM! I'VE **GOT** TO CHECK THIS OUT!

BUT WHERE CAN THE IMPULSES BE **COMING** FROM? THE RADIO IS SHUT OFF! AND DOCTOR COBBWELL DOESN'T HAVE ANY **OTHER** ELECTRICAL GADGETS OPERATING NOW!

HE'S PUTTING ON HIS COAT! THIS IS MY CHANCE--AS SOON AS HE LEAVES!

I HAVE TO LECTURE AT THE INSTITUTE NOW, PETER! I'LL BE BACK IN A FEW HOURS!

SLAM!

HE'S GONE! NOW TO SEE WHAT THIS IS ALL ABOUT!

HEY, NO ORDINARY RADIO HAD GADGETS LIKE *THAT* INSIDE OF IT! *THERE'S* WHERE THE IMPULSES ARE COMING FROM--EVEN WITH THE SET OFF!

THAT *DOES* IT! NOW I'M THRU KIDDIN' AROUND!

NOW *SPIDER-MAN* IS GONNA TAKE ANOTHER LOOK-SEE AT THE TINKERER'S SHOP!

THE PLACE IS CLOSED FOR THE DAY! WELL, THAT WON'T STOP *ME!*

I'M GETTING THOSE SAME STRANGE IMPULSES AGAIN! THEY'RE COMING FROM BELOW!

WOW! NO INNOCENT LITTLE REPAIR SHOP EVER HAD A BASEMENT WORKROOM LIKE *THAT* BEFORE! IT'S MORE LIKE A CONCRETE-REINFORCED *DUNGEON!*

LUCKY THE DOOR'S OPEN! GUESS THEY'RE NOT EXPECTIN' VISITORS!

AND, INSIDE THE ISOLATED WORKROOM...

YES! OUR ELECTRONIC SPY DEVICES, HIDDEN IN RADIOS BELONGING TO IMPORTANT EARTHLINGS, HAVE EN-ABLED US TO LEARN MUCH ABOUT THEIR STRENGTHS AND WEAKNESSES, BEFORE WE *ATTACK* THIS UNSUSPECTING PLANET!

QUIET! I AM PROCESSING THE LATEST PICTURES RELAYED BACK TO US BY OUR PIN-POINT TV SPY DEVICE WHICH YOU PLANTED IN THE RADIO OF A MILITARY LEADER!

YOU HAVE DONE YOUR WORK WELL, TINKERER! WE ARE ALMOST READY TO STRIKE!

5

HOW CLEARLY WE CAN HEAR AND SEE! MY DEVICES NEVER FAIL!

SILENCE! I MUST REMEMBER WHAT THEY SAY!

I SUMMONED YOU, COLONEL, TO DISCUSS OUR PLANS FOR THE DEFENSE OF OUR EASTERN SEABOARD IN CASE OF A SURPRISE ATTACK BY ANY HOSTILE FORCE...

SO THAT'S WHAT IT'S ALL ABOUT! THEY'RE ENEMY ALIENS FROM ANOTHER PLANET, USING SOME SORT OF EERIE SPY DEVICES WHICH THEY PLACE IN OUR RADIOS IN ORDER TO LEARN OUR MILITARY AND SCIENTIFIC SECRETS!

A SPY!

MY SPIDER INSTINCT WARNS ME-- SOMEONE IS BEHIND ME!

WHEW! NOT A SECOND TOO SOON! NOW, NO PLACE TO GO BUT INSIDE!

A COSTUMED EARTH CREATURE! SEIZE HIM!

IT'S NOT GONNA BE THAT EASY, BUDDY-BOY!

SEE WHAT I MEAN??

LOOK! HE CAN CLIMB SHEER WALLS!

HE IS NO ORDINARY EARTHLING! HE IS SPIDER-MAN! GET HIM!

IF HE ESCAPES WITH KNOWLEDGE OF OUR PLANS, WE ARE LOST!

HAH! THAT INVERTER MECHANISM, THROWN AT HIM LOOSENED HIS GRIP ON THE CEILING! HE'S FALLING!

NOW WE HAVE HIM! RENDER HIM HELPLESS!

WE CAN OVERWHELM HIM BY SHEER WEIGHT OF NUMBERS!

I'VE GOT **NEWS** FOR YOU! IT'S BEEN TRIED BEFORE!

HIS STRENGTH IS GREATER THAN WE SUSPECTED!

HE SHOOK US ALL OFF! A WEAPON! WE NEED A **WEAPON!**

WE **HAVE** A WEAPON! THE **TINKERER** IS NEVER UNPREPARED! **THIS** WILL STOP SPIDER-MAN!

OHHHH...

IT WOULD HAVE **KILLED** ANY NORMAL HUMAN-- BUT IT MERELY STUNNED **HIM!**

QUICKLY! PUT HIM INTO THE SPECIMEN CAGE BEFORE HE COMES TO!

THERE! NOTHING THAT LIVES CAN BREAK OUT OF THAT RESISTO-GLASS ENCLOSURE!

NOW, OUR FINAL PROBLEM IS TO FIND A SUITABLE WAY TO DISPOSE OF THE MEDDLER!

HE IS THE ONLY MORTAL ON EARTH WHO EVEN SUSPECTS OUR PRESENCE-- THE ONLY ONE WHO KNOWS OUR MASTER PLAN!

THERE IS NO QUESTION ABOUT IT! HE MUST BE DESTROYED! RELEASE THE AIR FROM THE RESISTO-GLASS PRISON!

7

WITHIN MINUTES, **SPIDER-MAN** WILL NO LONGER BE A MENACE TO US!

I'VE GOT TO MOVE **FAST!** THAT CONTROL PANEL ALSO OPENS AND SHUTS THIS CRAZY LITTLE MOUSETRAP!

THE AIR IS BEING FORCED OUT THRU THESE TINY HOLES! BUT INSTEAD OF KILLING ME, THESE LITTLE OPENINGS ARE GONNA **SAVE** ME!

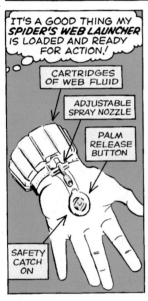

IT'S A GOOD THING MY **SPIDER'S WEB LAUNCHER** IS LOADED AND READY FOR ACTION!

CARTRIDGES OF WEB FLUID

ADJUSTABLE SPRAY NOZZLE

PALM RELEASE BUTTON

SAFETY CATCH ON

CAN'T AFFORD TO MISS! I'VE GOT TO LINE IT UP PERFECTLY WITH THE HOLE AND THE PROPER CONTROL PANEL BUTTON!

I'VE GOT THE SAFETY CATCH OFF--THE NOZZLE ON TARGET-- HAND STEADY--

BULL'S EYE!

IT **WORKED!** THE CAGE IS OPEN! **I'M FREE!**

LOOK! IT'S IMPOSSIBLE, BUT--HE'S LOOSE! **SPIDER-MAN** IS LOOSE!

WHO DO YOU THINK **YOU** ARE--THE TOWN CRIER??!

YOU **FOOL!** YOU JARRED MY ARM! I-I'VE DESTROYED OUR CONTROL PANEL!

IT WOULD TAKE **MONTHS** TO REBUILD THAT CONTROL PANEL! WE-- WE HAVEN'T THE TIME!

QUICK! LET US FLEE WHILE WE CAN! **SPIDER-MAN** IS TOO POWERFUL!

WAIT! DON'T LEAVE ME! DON'T ABANDON ME!

HOLD ON THERE, LAUGHING BOY! **YOU'RE** NOT GOING ANYWHERE!

THEY WERE JUST DOING THEIR DUTY TO WHATEVER PLANET THEY WERE FROM! BUT **YOU**, YOU TRAITOR--!

THIS SMOKE! THE BURNING CONTROL PANEL-- IT PUT THE WHOLE PLACE ON FIRE! STOP STRUGGLING, TINKERER! I'M TRYING TO **SAVE** YOU!

NO! LET ME **GO!** TAKE YOUR HANDS OFF ME! **NOBODY** TOUCHES THE **TINKERER!**

CAN'T SEE! THE SMOKE-- IT'S BLINDING ME-- CHOKING ME-- GOT TO GET AWAY!

JUST IN TIME! COULDN'T HAVE LASTED MUCH LONGER! BUT THE BUILDING IS A TOTAL WRECK! IT'LL BE REDUCED TO ASHES IN MINUTES!

I HEAR SIRENS! FIRE ENGINES! SOMEONE MUST HAVE TURNED IN AN ALARM! I'VE GOT TO DISAPPEAR!

LOOK! IT'S **SPIDER-MAN!**

MAYBE **HE** STARTED THE FIRE! BUT-- **WHY??**

9

MEANWHILE, A STRANGE SPACECRAFT BEGINS TO STREAK AWAY FROM EARTH...

SAFE AT LAST! PRESS THE BUTTON WHICH WILL DESTROY ALL OUR SPY DEVICES BY REMOTE CONTROL!

IT IS *DONE!* WE CAN NEVER AGAIN RETURN TO EARTH -- THEY WILL BE ON *GUARD* FROM THIS DAY ON!

AND, BACK AT THE LABORATORY OF DOCTOR COBBWELL...

I'VE RE-EXAMINED THE RADIO, AND IT'S PERFECTLY *NORMAL* NOW! NO DEVICES -- NO IMPULSES -- NOTHING!

HERE COMES DR. COBBWELL! HE LOOKS EXCITED!

MY BOY, I JUST SAW THE MOST STARTLING SIGHT!

AS I WAS RETURNING FROM THE LECTURE IN MY CAR, I GLANCED SKYWARD -- AND I COULD HAVE SWORN I SAW A *SPACE SHIP* OF SOME SORT, FADING INTO THE ATMOSPHERE!

REALLY? WHAT DID IT *LOOK* LIKE, SIR?

WELL, IT WAS SORT OF -- OHHH, WHAT AM I SAYING?? I MUST HAVE *IMAGINED* IT! NOBODY WOULD BELIEVE ME, ANYWAY! I HAVE NO *PROOF!* PEOPLE WILL THINK I'M A TYPICAL ABSENT-MINDED PROFESSOR! FORGET IT, PETER! LET'S GET BACK TO WORK!

SURE, DOC!

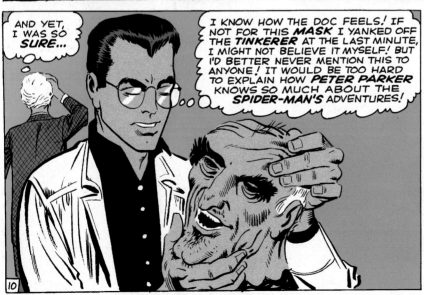

AND YET, I WAS SO *SURE*...

I KNOW HOW THE DOC FEELS! IF NOT FOR THIS *MASK* I YANKED OFF THE *TINKERER* AT THE LAST MINUTE, I MIGHT NOT BELIEVE IT MYSELF! BUT I'D BETTER NEVER MENTION THIS TO ANYONE! IT WOULD BE TOO HARD TO EXPLAIN HOW *PETER PARKER* KNOWS SO MUCH ABOUT THE *SPIDER-MAN'S* ADVENTURES!

10

the BEGINNING.. OF MORE AND GREATER *SPIDER-MAN* ADVENTURES STARTING NEXT ISSUE

BOY! I SURE GET THE *PICK* OF THE CROP!

JUST MY LUCK TO RUN INTO A JOKER *STRONG* ENOUGH TO CAUSE A *BRICK WALL* TO SHAKE WHEN HE USES HIS *POWER!*

TRY TO STOP ME *AGAIN,* AND YOU WON'T GET OFF SO *EASY!*

HE'S CUTTING OUT WITH THE *MONEY* HE STOLE!

I'VE GOTTA BE *CAREFUL!* THAT *VIBRATION GIZMO* OF HIS IS LIKE BEING KICKED BY A KING-SIZE *MULE!*

AND SPEAKING OF *KICKS*...

NOW DON'T GET THE FEELING I'M *MAD* AT YOU...

IT'S JUST THAT I HATE *ANYBODY* TO SKIP AROUND TOWN IN A *JAZZIER* COSTUME THAN *MINE!*

SPTOK!

BTAMMM!

ALL RIGHT... YOU *ASKED* FOR IT, *FOOL!*

SEE HOW YOU LIKE A PUNCH WITH A *TRIP-HAMMER VIBRATION SHOCK* ADDED!

I'M MORE INTERESTED IN MY STOLEN *WEALTH* THAN I AM IN BATTLING MY *INFERIORS!*

I *GAVE* YOU YOUR CHANCE TO ESCAPE UNHARMED... YOU WOULD HAVE BEEN WISER TO *TAKE* IT!

THE *VIBRO-SHOCK* UNIT ON MY FISTS MAKES MY BLOWS A *DOZEN TIMES* MORE POTENT THAN NORMAL!

FPOK!

UNNHHH...!

4.

NEXT TIME YOU'LL KNOW BETTER THAN TO CHALLENGE YOUR SUPERIORS!

MY VIBRO-BLAST POWER MAKES ME THE MOST INVINCIBLE HUMAN ON EARTH...AS YOU HAVE ALREADY LEARNED!

NO ONE CAN HURT ME WHEN I CAN DEFLECT ANY BLOW BY VIBRATING..

NO ONE...NOT EVEN THE SADDER BUT WISER SPIDER-MAN!

SECONDS LATER...

WOW-EEEE-~! NOW I KNOW HOW A BELL CLAPPER FEELS!

OF ALL THE GUYS TO TACKLE WITH A BAD ARM... I HADDA PICK HIM!

WELL, EVEN THOUGH HE GAVE ME MY LUMPS...AT LEAST I'LL HAVE SOME SHOTS OF HIM!

I'M GLAD I THOUGHT TO LEAVE MY CAMERA HERE...SET ON AUTOMATIC!

I GUESS THINGS COULD HAVE BEEN WORSE...

AT LEAST I'M LUCKY MY ARM WASN'T HURT WHILE I WAS ACTING LIKE A PART-TIME PUNCHING BAG!

HMM....IT'S HEALING PRETTY WELL NOW!

BUT, I'D STILL BETTER KEEP IT IMMOBILE FOR A LITTLE WHILE LONGER!

THE NEXT TIME I MEET THE SHOCKER...I WANNA BE SURE I CAN USE IT!

ALTHOUGH, WHEN HE SAID I'D BE HELPLESS AGAINST HIM WITH EVEN TWO ARMS...I HAVE A FEELING HE MEANT IT!

WHATEVER ELSE HE MAY BE, THAT JOE IS GONNA BE NO PUSHOVER!

WELL, I'D BETTER GET TO THE BUGLE AND SELL MY PIX TO JOLLY JONAH WHILE THEY'RE STILL NEWS!

HI, THERE, PETE! CAN I GIVE YOU A LIFT?

YOU SURE CAN, HARRY---IF YOU'RE HEADING TOWARDS THE BUGLE!

IT'S A DEAL! HOP IN...THERE'S SOMETHING I'VE BEEN WANTING TO TALK TO YOU ABOUT, ANYWAY!

GREAT! AT LEAST IT'LL TAKE MY MIND OFF THE SHOCKER!

I'VE GOT AN OFFER TO MAKE YOU, SON!

AN OFFER?

5

I FINALLY CONVINCED DAD THAT IT TAKES ME *TOO LONG* TO DRIVE TO AND FROM SCHOOL EACH DAY ALL THE WAY FROM OUR HOME IN WESTCHESTER!

DON'T TELL ME HE'S BUYING YOU A *WHIRLYBIRD*, HARR?

NOPE! EVEN *BETTER* THAN THAT, PETE!

YOUR OWN *PAD*, DAD? THAT'S *TERRIFIC!* BOY, WOULDN'T *I* GO FOR SOMETHING LIKE THAT!

HE GOT ME THE GREATEST LITTLE *APARTMENT*--- JUST A COUPLE OF BLOCKS FROM CAMPUS!

THAT'S WHAT I *HOPED* YOU'D SAY..!

THIS NEW LITTLE INGLENOOK OF MINE HAS *TWO*--COUNT 'EM... *TWO* BEDROOMS...!

AND, IF YOU WANTED TO *SHARE* THE PLACE WITH ME, PETE, I'LL BET WE COULD HAVE A *BALL!*

GOSH, HARRY... IT WOULD BE THE *END*--- BUT, I DON'T KNOW IF I COULD *AFFORD* IT!

YOU DIDN'T *READ* ME, SON! I SAID DAD *GOT* ME THE PLACE--- *HE'S* FOOTING THE RENT BILL!

SO WHAT'S THE *VERDICT*, MR.P.?

I'D LEAP AT IT IN A *SECOND*, HARRY...'CEPT FOR ONE THING!

I'VE GOT TO FIND OUT HOW *AUNT MAY* WOULD TAKE IT!

YOU KNOW, I'M THE ONLY RELATIVE SHE'S *GOT*... AND SHE'S SORT OF *DEPENDENT* ON ME!

LET ME CHECK IT OUT WITH *HER* FIRST AS SOON AS SHE GETS BACK! AND THANKS A *MILLION*, FELLA!

SURE THING, PETE! I'LL WAIT TILL I *HEAR* FROM YOU!

IT'S FUNNY THE WAY HARRY AND I HAVE BECOME REAL GOOD FRIENDS...WITHOUT HIM EVER SUSPECTING WHO I REALLY *AM*--- OR THAT I'M THE ONE WHO SAVED HIS *FATHER* WHEN HE WAS THE *GREEN GOBLIN* A WHILE BACK!

SEE YOU *LATER*, PETE!

BY THE WAY, NEXT TIME YOU SEE *MARY JANE*, LEMME KNOW AND I'LL CALL *GWEN!* THEY'D MAKE A *JAZZY* *DOUBLE-DATE!*

YOU *KNOW* IT!

HE'S SURE BEEN SEEING A LOT OF *GWEN* LATELY...!

NOW WHY SHOULD *THAT* BOTHER ME? *I'VE* HARDLY GIVEN HER THE TIME OF DAY SINCE *M.J.* MADE THE SCENE!

HELLO, PARKER!

BOY! SOMETIMES I THINK THE HARDEST THING IN THE WORLD IS FOR A FELLA TO JUST KNOW HIS OWN *MIND!*

HE DIDN'T *HEAR* ME!

PERHAPS IT'S JUST AS WELL! THIS IS MY CHANCE TO DO SOMETHING I'VE BEEN *WANTING* TO DO..!

I'VE ALWAYS *WONDERED* HOW HE MANAGES TO GET SO MANY EXCLUSIVE PHOTOS OF *SPIDER-MAN* IN ACTION!

I'M *POSITIVE* THERE'S SOME *CONNECTION* BETWEEN PARKER AND THAT WILY WEB-SLINGER...

AND *THIS* IS MY CHANCE TO DISGUISE MYSELF AS *PATCH* ONCE MORE, AND *TAIL* HIM TILL I LEARN HIS SECRET!

SOMETHING TELLS ME THERE'LL BE A GREAT *STORY* IN IT IF MY SUSPICIONS ARE CORRECT!

MR. JAMESON... MAY I *SEE* YOU FOR A MINUTE?

WASSAMATTER, PARKER? YOU FORGOT WHAT I *LOOK* LIKE?

NOBODY COULD FORGET A THING LIKE *THAT*..SIR!

AWRIGHT.. AWRIGHT! WHAT'S ON YOUR *MIND?*

WHAT'S ON MY *MIND* ISN'T FOR *SALE*, MR.J..

BUT I'VE GOT SOME *PHOTOS* FOR YOU THAT *ARE!*

IT'S ABOUT *TIME!*

6.

A NEW COSTUMED CREEP, EH? CALLS HIMSELF THE *SHOCKER*?

AND, AS FAR AS I KNOW... THESE ARE THE *ONLY* PHOTOS OF HIM *ANYWHERE*!

HE LOOKS LIKE A *NUT*... BUT HE'LL SURE SELL *NEWSPAPERS*!

THAT'S WHAT I *FIGURED*! SO HOW ABOUT SOME *BREAD*?

IF YOU'RE *HUNGRY*, GO TO THE DOWNSTAIRS *COMMISSARY*... AND CHARGE IT TO *ME*!

I WAS REFERRING TO *SCRATCH*... *LONG GREEN*... *FOLDING STUFF*... *MONEY*, TO YOU!

MONEY?? DON'T YOU *TRUST* ME, *PARKER*?

A QUESTION LIKE *THAT* CAN RUIN A GREAT RELATION-SHIP, *JJ*!

ALL RIGHT, YOU YOUNG *SHYLOCK*! I'LL HAVE BETTY BRANT GET YOU A CHECK!

ISN'T THIS *COFFEE-BREAK TIME* UP HERE?

COFFEE-BREAK! BIG DEAL! THE ONLY THING NO ONE TAKES IS A *WORK BREAK* IN THIS PLACE!

MISS BRANT! WHERE IN BLAZES IS THAT GIRL?

BLASTED GOLD-BRICKIN' LAZY NO-GOODS!

PAY NOW CRY LATER

THUMP! BAM!

EVERYONE TAKES *ADVANTAGE* OF ME!

HERE... *I'LL* WRITE OUT YOUR BLASTED CHECK!

I'M *FLATTERED*! I KNOW THOSE THINGS SLIP THROUGH YOUR FINGERS LIKE *GLUE*!

VER-RY FUNNY! NOW *TAKE OFF* WHILE I GET 'EM TO STOP THE PRESSES!

GXXX$: !!! EVEN THE *PRESS ROOM* DOESN'T ANSWER!

HOW LONG DO COFFEE-BREAKS *LAST* AROUND HERE, ANYWAY?

I OUGHT'A GIVE UP *PUBLISHING* AND START RAISIN' *COFFEE BEANS*!

THANKS FOR THE *DOUGH*, MR. JAMESON!

...KEEP *SMILIN'*, SWEETIE!

GOSH, I ALMOST *FORGOT*! AUNT MAY'S *TRAIN* WILL BE ARRIVING IN A FEW MINUTES!

I'VE GOT TO *MEET* HER AT THE STATION!

I CHANGED TO *PATCH* JUST IN TIME! PARKER'S LEAVING *NOW*...!

IF I CAN STAY WITH HIM *LONG* ENOUGH, HE'S *GOT* TO LEAD ME TO *SPIDER-MAN* SOONER OR LATER!

IT'S *IMPOSSIBLE* FOR ANYONE TO ALWAYS BE ON THE SPOT TO SNAP PHOTOS WHENEVER THAT WALL-CRAWLER IS AROUND... *UNLESS* THEY'RE WORKING *TOGETHER*!

AND, IF THEY *ARE*... I'M BOUND TO GET THE *EVIDENCE* IF I DON'T LOSE SIGHT OF *PARKER*!

THERE'S JUST TIME FOR ME TO *WALK* TO THE STATION!

BUT, PETER PARKER'S TIME MAY BE RUNNING *OUT*... FASTER THAN HE SUSPECTS! FOR, AT THAT MOMENT, IN ANOTHER PART OF TOWN...

EVERYTHING WENT *PERFECTLY*!

NOBODY'LL THINK TO LOOK FOR ME *HERE* IN AN OLD, ABANDONED LOFT BUILDING!

AND, IF THAT MEDDLESOME *SPIDER-MAN* BUTTS IN AGAIN, I'LL FINISH HIM FOR *GOOD* NEXT TIME!

IN FACT, IT MIGHT BE A *GOOD IDEA* TO DESTROY HIM... JUST TO SHOW THE *WORLD* HOW *POWERFUL* I AM!

NOW, IT'S TIME TO **COUNT** THE RESULTS OF MY DAY'S WORK... TO SEE IF MY POWER HAS **PAID OFF!**

AH! HUNDREDS AND HUNDREDS OF GREEN-BACKS! ALL **WON** BY THE MIGHT OF THE **SHOCKER!**

THIS IS WHAT I ALWAYS **DREAMED** OF... IN THE **OLD DAYS...**

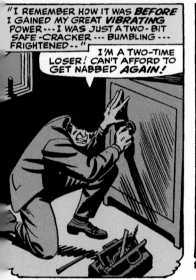

"I REMEMBER HOW IT WAS **BEFORE** I GAINED MY GREAT **VIBRATING** POWER... I WAS JUST A TWO-BIT SAFE-CRACKER... BUMBLING... FRIGHTENED..."

I'M A TWO-TIME LOSER! CAN'T AFFORD TO GET NABBED **AGAIN!**

OH **NO!** THERE WERE EXTRA GUARDS HERE TONIGHT! THEY **HEARD** THE NITRO!.!

I AIN'T GOT A **CHANCE!**

"SINCE I WAS GOOD WITH **TOOLS,** THEY PUT ME IN THE PRISON WORK-SHOP! BUT, I HAD ONLY **ONE THING** ON MY MIND... DURING ALL THOSE LONG, ENDLESS MONTHS..."

IF I EVER GET **OUT**... I'LL DO THINGS **DIFFER-ENT!** THEY'LL NEVER CATCH ME **AGAIN!**

I'LL DESIGN A SET OF TOOLS THAT CAN OPEN **ANY** SAFE.. SILENTLY ...IN **SECONDS!**

"BUT, WHILE WORKING ON MY TOOLS... A ONE-IN-A-MILLION **INSPIRATION** HIT ME...!"

A GADGET THAT CAN **SHAKE** A SAFE DOOR LOOSE WOULD BE BETTER THAN ANY-THING **ELSE!**

IF I CAN JUST FIND A WAY TO **CONTROL** THE SHOCK OF THE **VIBRATIONS**...!

LUCKILY, NO ONE HERE SUSPECTS WHAT I'M **REALLY** WORKING ON!

"THEN, MONTHS LATER... MY DEVICE WAS **READY!** IN THE DEAD OF NIGHT, WHEN MY CHANCES WERE THE GREATEST... I **USED** IT... AGAINST THE BRICK WALL, LEADING TO **FREEDOM**..!"

THIS IS **IT!** IT'S GOT TO WORK THE **FIRST** TIME... OR I'M **FINISHED!**

"IT **WORKED!** IT WORKED BETTER THAN I COULD HAVE **DREAMED!** THE WALL WAS SHATTERED WITHIN **SECONDS!** BUT, I WAS ALMOST INJURED TOO BADLY TO MAKE A RUN FOR IT..!"

I DIDN'T REALIZE THAT THE **FEEDBACK** WOULD BE SO STRONG! LUCKY I WASN'T **KILLED!**

BUT, I'LL WORRY ABOUT THAT **LATER**... ONCE I'M SAFELY **OUTTA** HERE!

8.

"AND, WORK ON IT I *DID!* HOUR AFTER HOUR...DAY AFTER DAY...WEEK AFTER WEEK--UNTIL FINALLY, JUST A SHORT TIME AGO--"

IT'S *FINISHED!*

THE FOAM-LINED FABRIC AND HEAVY BOOTS WILL *ABSORB* ANY FUTURE *SHOCKS!*

WHILE MY *BELT* WILL CONTAIN A LIFETIME *BATTERY* FOR A PERMANENT *POWER PACK!*

"BY LOCATING MY *VIBRA-SHOCK* UNITS WITHIN MY METAL *KNUCKLE PLATES*.. AND MAKING THEM *THUMB-OPERATED*---I KNEW I HAD MADE MYSELF *UN-BEATABLE!*"

AND, FROM THIS DAY ON, **THE SHOCKER** HAS PROVEN HIMSELF *SUPREME!*

NO ONE THAT LIVES CAN *STOP* ME!

MEANWHILE, AT THE NEWLY-CONSTRUCTED PENN STATION, MRS. *MAY PARKER* WAITS FOR HER BELOVED NEPHEW---

PETER SHOULD *BE* HERE AT ANY MINUTE!

OH DEAR.. I WONDER HOW HE'S GOING TO TAKE THE *NEWS* I HAVE FOR HIM..?

AUNT MAY!

THAT'S *HIM!*

PETER, DEAR, I'M SO GLAD TO...*OH!* YOUR *ARM!* WHAT *HAPPENED?*

NOTHING, AUNT MAY! JUST A LITTLE *SPRAIN!* IT'LL BE OKAY IN A DAY OR SO!

SAY! YOU LOOK *WONDERFUL!* THE REST MUST HAVE BEEN *GOOD* FOR YOU!

HOW WILL I *EVER* BRING MYSELF TO *SAY* IT--

YES, DEAR...I HAD A *WONDERFUL* TIME! BUT NOW---THERE'S SOMETHING I MUST *TELL* YOU---!

CAN IT *WAIT* JUST A SEC, AUNT MAY? I'VE GOT A REAL IMPORTANT MATTER TO DISCUSS WITH *YOU!*

GOSH! WHY THE *TEARS?* WHAT'S *WRONG?*

NOTHING, PETER! IT JUST THAT I'M SO *WORRIED* ABOUT YOU..!

WORRIED? WHY??

I KNOW HOW *DEPENDENT* YOU ARE UPON ME, DEAR, AND... *OH,* I'VE JUST *GOT* TO TELL YOU--!

MRS. *WATSON* IS SO LONELY SINCE *MARY JANE* MOVED AWAY... AND, SHE WANTS ME TO COME AND *STAY* WITH HER!

I'D *LOVE* TO DO IT... BUT IT WOULD MEAN LEAVING *YOU* ALL ALL ALONE AT HOME...!

IF ONLY I HAD THE *NERVE* TO TELL HER THAT I WANT TO MOVE OUT--TO BE ON MY OWN....!

WAIT A *MINUTE!* WHAT DID SHE SAY..??

YOU WANT TO MOVE IN WITH *MRS. WATSON?* BUT...YOU'VE BEEN WORRIED ABOUT LEAVING *ME* ALONE?!!

OH, PETER... I WAS *AFRAID* YOU'D TAKE IT THIS WAY! I..I DIDN'T WANT TO *UPSET* YOU!

UPSET ME? MRS. MAY PARKER, IT'S TIME YOU THOUGHT OF *YOURSELF* FOR A CHANGE!

STAYING WITH YOUR FRIEND, MRS. WATSON, WOULD BE JUST WHAT YOU *NEED!* YOU'D HAVE *COMPANY*... AND SOMEONE WHO'D ALWAYS *BE* THERE TO LOOK AFTER YOU WHEN YOU NEED IT MOST!

BUT, WHAT ABOUT *YOU,* DEAR? WHAT WOULD *YOU* DO?

I'M NOT A *CHILD* ANY MORE, AUNT MAY...IT'S *TIME* I WAS GETTING OUT ON MY OWN! I'LL SHARE AN APART- MENT WITH *HARRY OSBORN,* ONE OF MY CLASSMATES!

AND THAT MEANS YOU CAN SELL THE HOUSE...AND HAVE ENOUGH MONEY TO LIVE COMFORTABLY FOR THE NEXT FEW *YEARS!*

I'M SO HAPPY... THAT YOU'RE *TAKING* IT LIKE THIS...

THUS, A SHORT TIME LATER...

MAY, DEAR! HOW *WONDERFUL* YOU LOOK! COME IN AND TELL ME ALL ABOUT YOUR TRIP!

HELLO, MRS. WATSON! HI, MARY JANE! AUNT MAY HAS SOME- THING TO *TELL* YOU!

OH, *ANNA* DEAR... I'VE THE MOST *THRILL- ING* NEWS..!

...IT'S ALL RIGHT WITH *PETER* IF I MOVE *IN* WITH YOU!

I *TOLD* YOU IT WOULD BE! YOU'VE *ALWAYS* WORRIED ABOUT THAT BOY MUCH TOO MUCH!

AS FOR *YOU,* YOUNG LADY, WHAT SAY WE SKIP OVER TO THE *SILVER SPOON* TO CELEBRATE?

CELEBRATIONS ARE MY FAVORITE PEOPLE, DAD! LET'S CUT OUT!

HI, MARY JANE! WHERE'D YA DIG UP THE SON OF FRANKENSTEIN?

BELA LUGOSI *RENTED* HIM TO ME! BUT, DON'T GET HIM RILED 'TILL *AFTER* HE'S PAID FOR MY SODA, HEAR?

ANYWAY, WHAT'S *SHAKIN',* TIGER?

NOTHING MUCH! WE WERE JUST GETTING SET TO SPIN A FEW PLATTERS!

C'MON *IN!* THE STRAWS'RE ON *ME!*

WOW! WHO'S THAT *DOLL* DANCING OVER TH...HEY!

IT'S *GWEN!* I DIDN'T *RECOGNIZE* HER AT FIRST! LOOK AT HER *GO!*

HMM-- GWEN'S NOT *BAD,* DAD! NOT *GOOD,* MAYBE--BUT NOT *BAD!*

BUT, WHY AM I SO *SURPRISED?* I NEVER *FIGURED* HER FOR THE *WALL- FLOWER* TYPE!

BEFORE I FORGET, I WANTED TO *TELL* YOU TWO...

FLASH'S *FAREWELL PARTY* IS JUST ABOUT ALL SET! WE'LL HOLD IT RIGHT *HERE,* AT THE SILVER SPOON, WHEN HE GETS HIS INDUCTION DATE!

WE WANT IT TO BE A REAL *BLAST!* HE'S THE FIRST ONE OF THE CROWD TO BE *DRAFTED!*

YEP! WE'VE GOTTA DO IT UP *RIGHT* FOR OL' FLASH!

MMM MMM! THERE'S SOMETHING ABOUT A MALE IN *UNIFORM!* IT'S *WOW* CITY!

I WONDER HOW A *SPIDEY* COSTUME WOULD GRAB HER?

10.

HEY, GANG... DIDJA SEE THE BUGLE'S *EXTRA?*

SOME NUT NAMED THE *SHOCKER* MADE A *MONKEY* OUTTA SPIDER-MAN!

YEAH? *THAT'LL* BE THE DAY!

BUT, THERE'S *PICTURES* 'N EVERYTHING!

PROBABLY *FAKES!* OR ELSE SPIDEY WASN'T EVEN *TRYIN'!*

FAR AS *I'M* CONCERNED, *NOBODY* CAN BEAT THE OL' WEB-SLINGER!

DAILY BU... SHOCKER SMASHES SPIDER-MAN!

POOR FEARLESS *FLASH!* HE'S PROBABLY SPIDER-MAN'S BIGGEST BOOSTER! BUT, IF HE EVER FOUND OUT WHO SPIDEY REALLY *IS...* FORGET IT!

READY TO DIVE INTO A TWO-SCOOPER WITH ME NOW, M.J.?

NOT WHILE THE *JUKE* IS JUMPIN', DAD! SINCE YOU CAN'T SHAKE UP A STORM WITH YOUR *WING* IN A SLING, I'LL TAKE A RAIN CHECK TILL THE *COINS* RUN OUT!

IT'S JUST AS *WELL!* I WANNA LOOK FOR THE *SHOCKER,* ANYWAY!

I'LL BE TAKING OFF, SOON!

HAVE A HAPPY!

SAY, HARRY... REMEMBER THAT *OFFER* YOU MADE ME THIS MORNING?

WELL I HOPE YOU DON'T *SNORE,* SON!

HEY! YOU MEAN IT WAS OKAY WITH YOUR *AUNT?* MAN... THAT'S THE LIVIN' END!

WELL, WHAT ARE YOU STANDIN' *AROUND* FOR? GO HOME AND PACK, JACK!

HOW ABOUT *DANCING* WITH A LADY, MR. OSBORN?

THIS IS MY CHANCE TO TAKE OFF AFTER THE *SHOCKER!*

KEEP A CANDLE IN THE WINDOW FOR ME, ROOMMATE!

AND THAT'S *THAT!* BOY, GWEN NEVER LOOKED MORE *GORGEOUS*-- BUT SHE SURE DIDN'T KNOCK HERSELF OUT FALLIN' ALL *OVER* ME!

WHAT'S *WRONG* WITH ME, ANYWAY? WITH A BOMBSHELL LIKE *M.J.* IN THE PICTURE, I'M *STILL* NOT SATISFIED!

IT'S JUST THAT THERE'S SOMETHING ABOUT GWEN THAT *SINKS* ME... OR IS IT BECAUSE SHE'S MORE "HARD TO GET"?

NUTS! NEXT THING I'LL BE WRITING TO *DEAR ABBY!*

I'D BETTER SWITCH TO *SPIDEY,* AND DO SOME *WEB-SWINGING!*

HMMM! PARKER LOOKS LIKE HE'S OUT FOR *MORE* THAN JUST AN EVENING STROLL!

I'VE A HUNCH *PATCH* IS ABOUT TO LEARN HIS CONNECTION WITH *SPIDER-MAN* AT LAST!

AND THEN, EXACTLY SIXTY SILENT SECONDS LATER ---

THERE'S *SPIDEY...* IN THAT ALLEY!

BUT... WHAT BECAME OF PETER PARKER?

UH OH! MY *SPIDER-SENSE* IS TINGLING LIKE *MAD!* SOMEONE'S *WATCHING* ...NEARBY!

IT'S *PATCH*...THE STOOL-PIGEON!

IF HE SAW ME WALTZ *IN* HERE AS PETE PARKER... AND SEES ME *NOW* AS SPIDEY... HE WON'T HAVETA BE AN *EINSTEIN* TO DIG MY *SECRET!*

I'VE GOTTA *THINK* OF SOMETHING --- BUT *FAST!*

FOSWELL... YOU'RE A FAT-HEADED, FEEBLE-MINDED *FOOL!*

HERE I'VE BEEN WONDERING WHERE PARKER *WENT* TO... AND THE ANSWER'S BEEN STARING ME IN THE *FACE* ALL THE TIME!

I SHOULD HAVE *GUESSED* IT... HE DIDN'T GO *ANY-WHERE...*

PARKER IS SPIDER-MAN!

AND I'M THE ONLY ONE WHO *KNOWS* IT!

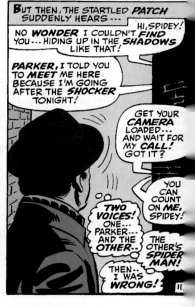

BUT THEN, THE STARTLED *PATCH* SUDDENLY HEARS ---

NO *WONDER* I COULDN'T *FIND* YOU... HIDING UP IN THE *SHADOWS* LIKE THAT!

HI, SPIDEY!

PARKER, I TOLD YOU TO *MEET* ME HERE BECAUSE I'M GOING AFTER THE *SHOCKER* TONIGHT!

GET YOUR *CAMERA* LOADED... AND WAIT FOR MY *CALL!* GOT IT?

YOU CAN COUNT ON *ME,* SPIDEY!

TWO VOICES! ONE... PARKER... AND THE OTHER..

THE OTHER'S *SPIDER-MAN!*

THEN... I WAS *WRONG!*

11

AND REMEMBER.. I GET 50% OF THE *MONEY* YOU RECEIVE FOR SELLING THE *PICTURES!*

DON'T WORRY! YOU'RE THE *ONE* GUY I'M NOT ABOUT TO START *CHEATING!*

LUCKY I CAN CHANGE THE TONE OF MY *VOICE* BY RAISING AND LOWERING MY *FACE MASK!*

NOW FOR A *QUICK CHANGE* WHILE I KEEP *TALKING!*

GOOD OL' *SPIDER SPEED..* I COULDN'T *DO* THIS WITHOUT IT!

WHAT IF YOU CAN'T *BEAT* THE SHOCKER, SPIDEY?

YOU KIDDIN'? JUST TAKE THE *PIX*, PARKER... *I'LL* DO THE REST!

WHEW! IF I GET *AWAY* WITH THIS, IT'LL BE A *MIRACLE!*

HE'S STILL LISTENING, ON THE OTHER SIDE OF THE WALL!

JUST *STAY* THERE, PATCH... WHILE I RIG UP A *WEB-DUMMY* OF OL' *SPIDER-MAN!*

I'LL HANG IT BY ITS OWN WEBBING, AND GIVE IT A *SHOVE* TO START IT SWINGING!

YOU DIDN'T TELL ME WHERE YOU'RE *GOING*, SPIDEY?

NUTS! HE'S ALWAYS SWINGING OFF WITHOUT *ANSWERING!*

HOW *ABOUT* THAT! I WAS *DEAD WRONG!* PARKER IS STILL *STANDING* THERE WHILE THE WEB-HEAD SWINGS AWAY!

WELL, THAT'S *IT!* I'M NOT *BRANDO*, BUT I HOPE I ACTED GOOD ENOUGH TO FOOL MY ONE-MAN AUDIENCE!

I ALMOST MADE A KING-SIZED *JACKASS* OUT OF MYSELF! HOW COULD I HAVE THOUGHT A TEEN-AGED NOBODY LIKE *PARKER* COULD ACTUALLY BE *SPIDER-MAN!*

WELL, ANYWAY, I FOUND OUT HOW THE KID GETS THOSE EXCLUSIVE *PHOTOS!* HE'S GOT A *DEAL* COOKING WITH SPIDER-MAN! THE MASKED MAN *TIPS HIM OFF* WHEN HE'S GOING INTO ACTION... AND THEN PARKER SPLITS THE MONEY HE GETS FOR THE PIX WITH *SPIDEY!*

IT *STILL* DOESN'T SOUND *KOSHER*, THOUGH! YOU'D THINK A GUY LIKE *SPIDER-MAN* COULD MAKE ALL THE DOUGH HE *WANTS!*

BUT, WHY *FIGHT* IT? I *SAW* THEM... AND *HEARD* 'EM WITH MY OWN EARS!

OH, *BRO*-THER! WAS *THAT* A CLOSE ONE!

FOR A *WHILE* THERE IT LOOKED LIKE I COULD JUST KISS MY "SECRET IDENTITY BIT" BYE-BYE FOR *GOOD!*

WELL, NOW THAT *SHOW TIME'S* OVER--!

I'VE ABOUT *HAD* IT WITH THAT BLAMED *SLING!*

MY ARM'S *STILL* A LITTLE SORE, BUT WHAT THE HEY!

WHO EVER OF A SWINGIN' SUPER-HERO *BABYING* HIMSELF?

12.

13.

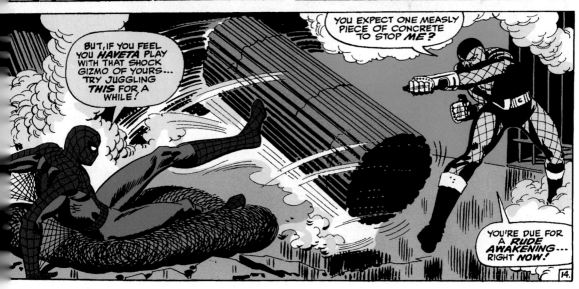

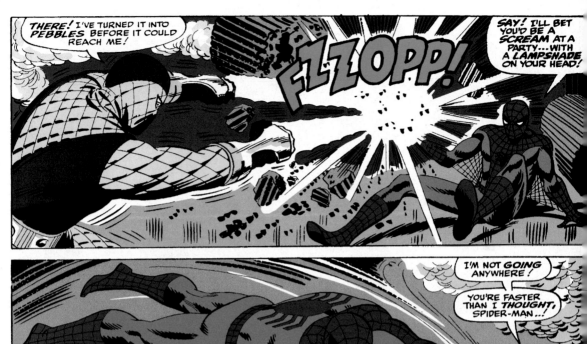

16.

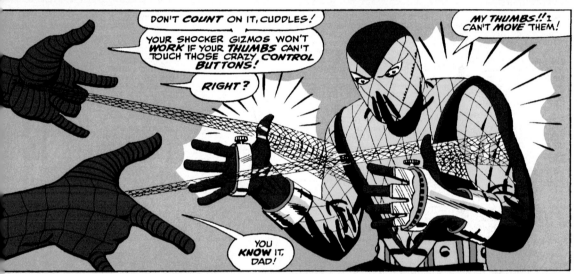

A FEW SECONDS LATER...

THANKS FOR THE *PICTURES* SHOCKY!

NOW YOU'LL BE NICE AND COMFY THERE UNTIL THE *POLICE* ARRIVE, WON'T YOU?

SMILE, DARN IT! THAT *WEBBING'S* MORE EXPENSIVE THAN YOU *THINK!*

IT'S FUNNY... WITHOUT HIS LITTLE *WRIST-SHOCKER SET*, HE'S JUST ANOTHER CHEAP HOOD!

OH, WELL... IT SURE IS A *PLEASURE* TO HAVE EVERYTHING TURN OUT A-OKAY FOR A CHANGE!

I CAUGHT MY MAN.. GOT MY PIX... AND MY *ARM* FEELS AS GOOD AS NEW AGAIN! IT'S *WOWVILLE!*

NOT ONLY IS *SPIDEY* DELIGHTED WITH THE WAY THINGS WORKED OUT, BUT EVEN *STAN* AND *JOHN* ARE RELIEVED FOR ONCE... AND, WE'VE A HUNCH THAT *YOU* DON'T MIND YOURSELF... RIGHT, TIGER?

ANYWAY, THE NEXT MORNING HERALDS THE DAWN OF A NEW DAY... AND OF A BRAND NEW CHAPTER IN THE LIFE OF OUR FRIENDLY, NEIGHBORHOOD SPIDER-MAN...

I AWOKE EVEN BEFORE THE *ALARM* WENT OFF!

IN FACT, I'VE BEEN WAKING UP ALL NIGHT!

I'M JUST TOO *EXCITED* TO SLEEP!

TODAY'S THE DAY I PACK MY GEAR AND MOVE IN WITH *HARRY!*

MY OWN PAD AT *LAST!* GOSH... I CAN HARDLY *BELIEVE* IT!

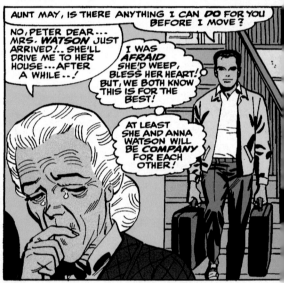

AUNT MAY, IS THERE ANYTHING I CAN *DO* FOR YOU BEFORE I MOVE?

NO, PETER DEAR... MRS. *WATSON* JUST ARRIVED!... SHE'LL DRIVE ME TO HER HOUSE... AFTER A WHILE..!

I WAS *AFRAID* SHE'D WEEP, BLESS HER HEART! BUT, WE BOTH KNOW THIS IS FOR THE BEST!

AT LEAST SHE AND ANNA WATSON WILL BE *COMPANY* FOR EACH OTHER!

NOW *LOOK*, YOUNG LADY! I DON'T WANT TO SEE MY BEST GAL WITH *TEARS* IN HER EYES!

REMEMBER, AUNT MAY... IT'S NOT AS THOUGH WE'RE SAYING *GOOD-BYE!* WE'RE JUST CHANGING OUR *ADDRESSES*--- THAT'S ALL!

PETER, DEAR... PROMISE ME YOU'LL PHONE WHENEVER YOU CAN... AND COME TO *VISIT* WHEN YOU HAVE TIME!

AND TAKE GOOD *CARE* OF YOURSELF! BE SURE TO GET ENOUGH *SLEEP*... AND EAT PLENTY OF NOURISHING *FOOD!* YOU KNOW HOW *FRAGILE* YOU ARE!

REMEMBER TO WEAR YOUR *SWEATER* WHEN IT'S CHILLY... AND DON'T GET YOUR FEET WET!

AND, BE CARE-FUL WHOM YOU CHOOSE FOR *FRIENDS!* I DON'T EVER WANT MY PETER TO ASSOCIATE WITH *ROUGHNECKS*--!

JUST YOU STAY AS PRETTY AS YOU ARE... AND DON'T WORRY ABOUT A *THING!*

AND REMEMBER--- NO MORE *TOUCH FOOTBALL*---OR *KARATE* PRACTICE!

OH, PETER, PETER... YOU ALWAYS *COULD* FIND A WAY TO MAKE ME SMILE!

AND THEN, FINALLY...

I KNOW HOW YOU FEEL, DEAR! IT WAS THE SAME WHEN *MARY JANE* MOVED AWAY FROM HOME!

THAT'S WHY I'M SO *HAPPY* YOU'RE COMING TO STAY WITH ME NOW!

HE'S ALL THE FAMILY I *HAVE*! I PRAY HE'LL BE ALL RIGHT---HE'LL BE HAPPY---ON HIS OWN!

I NEVER *KNEW* MY MOTHER.. BUT SHE *COULDN'T* HAVE BEEN SWEETER... OR GENTLER... OR MORE *WONDERFUL*...THAN AUNT MAY!

THE WAY SHE ALWAYS *WORRIED* ABOUT EVERY LITTLE THING...!

THAT'S WHY I COULD NEVER... *NEVER*... LET HER LEARN THE TRUTH... ABOUT *SPIDER-MAN*!

A SHORT TIME LATER, IN A PLEASANT APARTMENT BUILDING, JUST A STONE'S THROW AWAY FROM CAMPUS..

WELCOME TO THE PAD, LAD!

IT'S NOT THE *TAJ MAHAL*... BUT IT'S BETTER THAN A *TENT*!

YOU MEAN... ALL THIS IS *OURS*??

IT'S *OUT OF SIGHT*, HARR...!

--AND, IN *LIVING COLOR*, TOO!

GLAD YOU *LIKE* IT, MR. PARKER!

I'VE GOTTA GO *OUT* FOR A WHILE... SO MAKE YOURSELF AT HOME!

SURE THING, PAL! THIS IS GONNA TAKE A LITTLE GETTING *USED* TO!

BUT, HOW COME THERE'S NO *BUTLER*?

SORRY ABOUT THAT! SEE YOU LATER, ROOM-MATE!

BUT, FOR LONG, LONELY SECONDS AFTER THE DOOR HAS CLOSED BEHIND THE EBULLIENT HARRY, PETER PARKER STANDS MOTIONLESS, SILENTLY CLOAKED IN HIS OWN SOMBER THOUGHTS...

I SHOULD BE CLICKING MY HEELS AND DOING *CARTWHEELS* RIGHT NOW! I'VE FINALLY GOTTEN WHAT I *WANTED*...

I'M ON MY *OWN* AT LAST...SHARING A PAD WITH A PAL!

SO WHY THIS *LETDOWN* FEELING? WHY THIS MOOD OF *DEPRESSION* THAT I CAN'T SEEM TO SHAKE?

IS IT JUST A NATURAL FEELING OF *HOMESICKNESS*? OR, IS IT SOMETHING *DEEPER*!

ON THAT FATEFUL DAY ---WHEN I BECAME *SPIDER-MAN*--- PERHAPS *MORE* THAN THAN A *PHYSICAL* CHANGE WAS WROUGHT...

PERHAPS, IN SOME STRANGE, MYSTERIOUS WAY...WHEN I GAINED ANOTHER IDENTITY...I LOST THE CAPACITY... FOR *HAPPINESS*!

next:

MORE POWERFUL! MORE DANGEROUS! MORE DEADLY THAN EVER!

THE RETURN OF KRAVEN THE HUNTER!

20.